G000055718

his book takes you through the West Country to the rest of the world, with fifteen gruesome individuals ranging from Lord Berkeley to Barefoot Mary, showing the be in your blood, regardless of your social standing or gender.

To Marcus, Lord, Whi + David

Lord Berkeley the Viking

Vikings were the pirates of Scandinavia, crossing the seas in search of land to loot. One of the greatest Vikings was the descendant of King Harding of Hardanger, Norway. He joined forces with fellow Viking William the Conquer to invade southern England from Normandy in 1066.

As a reward for his loyalty and support, Harding was appointed Reeve, or Governor, of the castle at Bristol – the second largest in the new kingdom after the tower of London. He set about fortifying it with stone brought up the River Avon.

The castle was in a prominent position on high ground surrounded by the Avon and Frome rivers on three sides and was to be used as a military base to control the Welsh hoards attempting to come over the border into England, as well as being the point from which Richard de Clare, the second earl of Pembroke, would invade Ireland with an army of 200.

In 1102 the family supported Baldwin I, the king of Jerusalem, in capturing Jaffa from the mighty Saladin in the Crusades and were awarded Crusaders crosses to sport on their family Coat of Arms. They lived on a street outside Bristol's city walls, which they named Baldwin Street after the crusader king.

In 1154, as a reward for protecting the young prince who was later to become King Henry II, the Hardings were granted 50 huge West Country estates stretching from Berkeley Castle in Gloucestershire to Berkeley Square, London. Robert Fitz Harding became Lord Berkeley. With the vast income produced by their manors, the newly titled family set about building St. Mary Redcliffe and St. Augustines Abbey from Dundry quarry stone. The Berkeley coat of arms can still be seen on the Norman archway.

By 1240, the Berkeleys had turned their attention to expanding the port of Bristol by building new quays and altering the course of the River Frome to run through the city centre.

In the 16th century, King Henry VIII visited Gloucestershire and took a fancy to Lady Mary Berkeley, by whom he fathered two illegitimate sons (see *Lord Stuckley the Lion-tamer* for more on this).

In 1597, together with descendants of the Dukes of Normandy, the de Clifford family, the Berkeleys decided to return to their marauding heritage to pay off gambling debts. They took a large fleet and 4,000 men to invade the Portuguese Azores, an archipelago of islands off the African coast. There they planned to capture the Spanish treasure galleons returning to Cádiz on Spain's most southerly tip. Sadly, organisation wasn't their strong point and they missed the Spanish fleet by just a couple of days, returning to England with nothing more than a few pigs.

In 1664 Lord John Berkeley of Bruton, Somerset was appointed Captain of the Guard and sailed with the brother of King Charles II, the Duke of York and Albany, to the Dutch colony then known as New Amsterdam. The Duke renamed it New York and Berkeley was appointed Governor of New Jersey, which he later sold to Bristol Quakers led by the Penn family of Redcliffe, who later moved to a part of America they named Pennsylvania.

Berkeley was also granted a large estate near Marble Arch London. He developed the estate into Berkeley square, next to Pall Mall, where Nell Gwyn, Charles II's favourite of 18 mistresses, resided.

By now an Admiral, Berkeley led his crew into the Caribbean from Carolina on board *The Berkeley Galley* in 1690. During the voyage they lost crewman James Tiche overboard whilst chasing Spanish galleons. James left behind a wife and a young son. On their return Admiral Lord Berkeley moved the widowed Mary and her son Edward into Bristol. At Berkeley's behest, Mary and her son moved into 12 Guinea Street, Redcliffe. In the former Quaker hospital she was to look after his sea captain Edmund Saunders.

Here young Edward grew up surrounded by the sailors, ruffians and press gangs that frequented the harbour-side taverns. Thanks to this rough and ready upbringing, Edward was quick to learn the trade that would make him one of the most successful and notorious pirate of the 17th century.

Forkbeard sails up the Avon Gorge to attack Bristol Castle

Blackbeard the Merciless

Edward Teach, also known as Edward Tiche or Edward Thatch, was an exceptionally tall youth with dark piercing eyes, cauliflower ears, a bashed-in nose and a very loud voice. Following in his father's footsteps, young Edward went to sea at an early age, first serving on a British ship in the War of the Spanish Succession before turning to piracy, as did many of the so-called privateers after Britain withdrew from the War in 1713.

He kept control aboard ship by inviting captured captains to join him for a drink in his cabin and offering them rum laced with gunpowder, making sure they sat at the opposite end of the table. When he had the information he wanted he would shoot them in the groin with a pair of pistols he kept strapped under the table. Not surprisingly, his crews were disinclined to upset him.

Once, when his ship had struck a reef, in order to avoid paying his crew Teach abandoned it and disappeared with the treasure; then bought another ship, recruited another crew and began pirating again.

His big chance came when he was sailing off the French island of Martinique under Captain Benjamin Hornigold in November 1717. They intercepted a large slave ship out of Nantes, France (*La Concorde*) that was overcrowded with 500 black slaves. It had sailed direct to the sugar islands from the slave port of Benin on the African Guinea coast and the crew were tired and suffering from small pox carried by the slaves who in turn were manacled in cramped conditions below decks. It did not put up much resistance.

A French Admiralty report, found at the Aix-en-Province Centre des archives d'Outremer, details the incident. In a document dated November 17, 1717 Charles Mesnier, Intendant of Martinique, describes the capture of la Concorde de Nantes as it was

> *"...attacked by two boats of English pirates. One of 12 guns and the other of 8 guns armed with with 250 men controlled by Edouard Tiche of Bristol, English...."*

The Superintendent was particularly upset that Tiche/Teach had cut off the French captains lips and forced him to eat them in order to find out where he had hidden the bag of gold dust taken in Africa. The cabin boy was so traumatised by this barbaric act that he fetched it from a secret compartment in the bulkhead. Teach then set the French captain adrift in a small boat with the survivors of his crew, enabling them to sail on to the Colony, knowing that they would report the incident.

Thus started Blackbeard's reign of terror on the high seas. Teach was elected captain after Hornigold was overthrown by his crew, taking command of *La Concorde* and renaming her *Queen Anne's Revenge*. The *Queen Anne's Revenge* would remain his flagship for most of his career. His first act as captain was to sail to the nearby island of Nevis and sell the slaves to the Bristol plantation owners that controlled the island. He decided to keep one muscle-bound slave, called Caesar as his personnel bodyguard; Caesar stayed by his side until Blackbeard met his death. With the money from the sale Blackbeard began arming the big slaver with 40 large cannons, clearing the main deck and opening up the three slave decks below for contraband storage and more gun platforms. The Queen Anne's Revenge became a formidable fighting machine.

His reputation as the most notorious pirate was gained by installing fear; often he would intertwine long gunpowder fuses in his black beard, lighting them as he swung into action boarding enemy ships. Now on the rampage the sadistic pirate's true colours came out. Blackbeard and his men continued raiding, looting and womanising in the Caribbean. Soon, they were in desperate need of medical supplies to lessen the effects of the various venereal diseases they had contracted. Sailing north up the American coastline, Blackbeard's fleet of four ships – manned by four hundred sailors, the largest pirate crew in history – intercepted a supply ship from England bound for the colonies at Charlestown, Carolina. He took the supplies he needed from the hold and kept the crew as hostages, then blockaded the harbour.

In return for the release of the hostages the Governor of Charlestown, Charles Eden (ancestor of a future Prime Minister of Great Britain) allowed Blackbeard to continue his piracy provided he gave half the proceeds of his loot to the impoverished colony. With this sudden, new-found respectability Teach, now a friend of the Governor, decided to change his image. He wore fine silks, a powdered wig and strutted around the town. Then he began courting Mary Ormond, the 16 year-old daughter of a wealthy plantation owner, even though, as captain of his ship, he had previously 'married' young virgins fourteen times. These women were treated appallingly: when he tired of them he let the crew use them as they wished or strapped them up to a tree in the garden. His new bride, unfortunately, went the same way, but not before he had built a large house for her in an area called Bath, near Charlestown. The remains of the house are presently being excavated.

Eventually Eden came to Teach with information that a lone, heavily-laden Spanish treasure ship would be passing by unprotected. He suggested Teach should capture it – provided, of course, that he gave Eden half of the proceeds. The *Queen Anne's Revenge* ambushed the Spaniard and hoisted the pirate's flag, the Jolly Roger – black, with a red heart on it – which signified that no prisoners would be taken. None were. The treasure of 400 silver ingots was taken and Blackbeard sailed on triumphantly.

To the jealous Governor Spotswood of nearby Virginia this bloody act of piracy was the last straw. On November 24, 1718 he ordered ships of the Royal Navy, under the command of Captain Maynard in *The Pearl*, to seize Blackbeard at all costs. In the ensuing bloody confrontation Blackbeard suffered 22 sword cuts to his body but still struggled, even after he was shot in the stomach at point-blank rage. Dying, he signalled to Caesar to blow up the ship, but he failed to reach the barrels of gunpowder stored below decks. Blackbeard was decapitated by one of Maynard's crew, a Scotsman who wielded a two-handed claymore from behind. The pirate's head was displayed on the bowsprit of Maynard's ship and taken to Virginia. His headless torso swam around the ship chased by his old parrot, who had never left his side in 10 years.

Governor Spotswood would not pay out the £100 bounty which angered the crew and, to prevent the town being smashed up that night by the drunken sailors, it was taken down from a spike overlooking the quay and hidden. Legend has it that the skull was used as a ceremonial drinking goblet in the Raleigh Tavern, Williamsburg. Blackbeard's skull has recently been discovered, having remained in private hands for 300 years. It is now on display in the local museum.

To this day, in the plasterwork on the front of the house in Bristol where Edward Teach is reputed to have lived, you can still see an impression of his terrible face. Deep below in the cellar is the trapdoor that leads into the labyrinth of tunnels that linked into the Ostrich tavern.

Blackbeard's head is hoisted high

Governor Rogers the Seadog

> *"I took 'is treasure an' then gave 'im the sharp edge o' me cutlass."*

Another powerful Norman Plantagenet family arrived in England from Beaumont de Rogers, France. Travelling with William the Conqueror from their castle near Paris, they settled at Blandford Forum in Dorset where they built a manor house on the banks of the River Stour. Over the years the Rogers formed part of England's establishment, becoming Sheriffs, Members of Parliament and Justices of the Peace. By marrying into other land-owning families they increased their wealth and power.

In the Viking language the name Rogers is 'Hrothgar', which means 'seadog', so it is perhaps not surprising that in Elizabethan times Sir Richard Rogers was tried for piracy in Poole, Dorset. Although he had taken the precaution of hiding the smuggled goods in his family vault in Blandford church and offloading a large haul of brandy from his ship into the cellars of a local inn, the family felt so shamed by the public disgrace of his hanging that they sold their two thousand-acre estate to the Berkeley-Portman family, who rebuilt the Rogers' manor, now known as Bryanston School.

Meanwhile, Richard Rogers' brother Francis continued the family trade using Lulworth Cove on the Dorset coast as a base of operations. The isolated cove was popular amongst pirates as a place where all were welcome to trade stolen goods in sheltered waters.

The Rogers then re established themselves near the port of Bristol, where they became involved in various skulduggeries including the financing of early slave traders and using their ship *The Whetstone Galley* for minor acts of piracy. Ironically, these adventures came to an abrupt end when the ship was seized by French pirates off Bordeaux on its way back to Bristol from the African slaving port of Senegal, complete with its bounty of £1,000 in gold dust.

In time, the Rogers developed a marshy area belonging to Bristol Cathedral into an attractive space they named Queen Square. It soon became a fashionable place to live and Woodes Rogers, the eldest of seven sons, was born and brought up here.

The Rogers' social circle included a number of Quakers, one of whom was Thomas Goldney who owned a modest greengrocer's shop on Small Street.

Goldney went on to make a fortune by manufacturing slave manacles in his brass works on the River Frome. These items were highly prized by the feuding tribal rulers along the Golden Guinea coast of Africa, and were used as barter goods in exchange for fit young tribal men who were then transported to the new rapidly expanding American colonies by the 300-strong fleet of Bristol slave ships.

Goldney advanced Rogers £4,000, a vast sum of money in those days, to finance an expedition to seize Spanish treasure ships. The profits enabled Goldney to build a grotto in the grounds of his new mansion Goldney House, which still stands in Clifton today. He used the grotto as a place to store the remarkable natural treasures that the pirates brought back to him from all around the world.

Woodes Rogers' ship *The Duke* was a 320-ton beauty that sailed from the Grove in January 1708. Together with her sister ship *The Duchess*, onboard which his brother John was part of the crew, Rogers had 300 men under his command, made up of a handful of professional sailors and a ragtag assortment of ex-convicts and lay-abouts. Predictably, during their first port of call in Ireland, 60 crewmen were left behind because they overslept due to their drinking and womanising the night before.

Rogers' expedition was very well planned and although he was only 29 years old at the time, and had no experience of seamanship, he had a powerful presence and had gathered plenty of people around him with the right experience.

A very important member of the expedition was William Dampier, then aged 50 or more. Dampier had a reputation as a buccaneer and had sailed their

Governor Rogers inspects the Silver Candlestick in Bristol Cathedral

planned route before. In the company of British naval frigates, Rogers captained his ships south of the Azores, learning more seamanship alongside the Royal Navy vessels.

The two ships skirted the Falkland Islands on Christmas Day 1708, sailing around Cape Horn before travelling north up the Chilean coast. During the long voyage the crews practiced boarding unsuspecting ships and took some modest prizes. They put the Spanish prisoners they captured into the holds and freed the black slaves they found aboard the Spanish ships. Adding the freed slaves to his crews, Rogers ended up with a force of more than 1,000 men at arms and a fleet of more than 20 ships.

Concerned that the slaves, who he was training to fire weapons, would turn on him, he decided to give them a diversion and some practice by looting the Spanish port of Guayaquil in April 1709.

Sitting on his veranda in the sunshine, the Spanish Governor was horrified to see a horde of gun-waving men swarming up the hill towards him and immediately offered Rogers 40,000 ducats to call them off. But the men were uncontrollable, running amok, attacking women, stealing their jewellery and even digging skeletons out of their graves in order to make off with any valuables that had been buried with the bodies.

With difficulty, Rogers disciplined them and sailed north again. But retribution came upon the grave robbers as most of them died of an unidentified disease.

The ships were soon in desperate need of fresh water, and Dampier, brought on the expedition as navigator, proved his worth by steering them to a remote island, Juan Fernandez. On landing, Rogers was surprised to be greeted by a Scottish man dressed entirely in goat skins.

The castaway was Alexander Selkirk, a buccaneer who had been marooned on the island by Dampier for insubordination on a previous voyage after he demanded that the crew got a bigger share of the loot. Left alone with a Bible, some biscuits, tobacco and a pistol, he spent his time praying and making regular forays to the highest point on the island to look for a ship on the horizon. He was to have a long wait, having spent four years and four months on the island before Rogers' fleet arrived.

Selkirk had lived mainly off the goats who were plentiful on the island; drinking their milk, eating their meat and making clothes for himself out of their skins. But he was very lonely; as he later wrote: "*There were many sounds, but no voices*".

His own voice had become little more than a croak from want of use, but he was physically very fit.

When Dampier finally arrived and came ashore with a Bristol bulldog, Selkirk showed them that he could run faster than the dog. In truth, he seemed more a beast than a man.

After replenishing the ships' stores, Woodes Rogers headed north again to the coast of California, intending to intercept Spanish galleons. *La Incarnacion*, a French escort ship hired by the Spanish to protect their heavily laden ships, soon appeared over the horizon. Using harrying tactics against the much larger vessel, Rogers seized the ship, which was also full of treasure. Tragically his bother was killed in the process and Rogers was himself wounded in the face. Never a one to miss the opportunity for some drama, he used his own blood as ink to write orders for the crew to carry on the battle. Recovering fast, he realised that a huge Spanish treasure ship, the *Begonia*, was following behind *La Incarnacion*. Rogers quickly ordered his captured ships to form a line in front of the expected route of the galleon.

The Begonia was largely manned by British mercenaries who had their own personal treasure chests on board and were determined that in no way were they going to allow it to be captured. With more than 500 English cannon balls bouncing off its hull, the ship sailed straight through Rogers' fleet.

The Spaniards in South America were now alerted and, unable to return the way he had come, Rogers was obliged to try to circumnavigate the world. After months at sea, in desperate straits and forced to eat rats to survive, his fleet called at Guam, where they sold some of the ships and their captives in exchange for crucial supplies.

At last, in October 1711, The Duke and The Duchess sailed up the Thames with the captured French treasure ship, which had been renamed *The Bachelor* after one of their sponsors.

One remarkable relic of this four-year voyage is a pair of silver candlesticks. The candlesticks were donated to Bristol Cathedral's treasury by one of the voyage's sponsors and can be seen there today in the Lady Elder chapel.

On his return, the restless Rogers was heavily in debt because he only earned £150 from his voyage, while his seamen received just £50 after four years of risking their lives. Rogers wrote a book about his adventures called *A Voyage to the South Seas*.

The tale attracted the attention of Daniel Defoe, who was taking the waters in the spa at Hot Wells in Bristol. All his life Defoe had been looking for a great story, and at last he had found it. A meeting was arranged at the Llandoger Trow Inn and as a result Defoe romanticised Rogers' book and was inspired

The marooned castaway discovers a footprint in the sand

by the story of Alexander Selkirk to create the character Robinson Crusoe.

Sadly for Selkirk, Defoe got the profits from the book and that castaway received nothing. This was true to form, since Defoe, born in 1659 as the son of a London butcher, had often walked the thin line between right and wrong, and as a result had served time in prison. The Selkirk story made his name. He gave the character the name Robinson after seeing an inscription on a tombstone whilst hiding from the Roundheads in Chipping Sodbury.

The book was then deemed the best of its kind in any language, blending fact and fiction so seamlessly that the reader truly believed every word.

After years ashore Selkirk once again became a sailor. He was had up for rowdy behaviour in the seedy bars of Marsh Street, Bristol, where sailors met, got drunk and partied. He gave the court Rogers' address in Queens Square and was last seen heading for Plymouth with a plain girl of Bedminster in tow. He eventually died of disease aboard *HMS Weymouth* off the African coast in 1721.

William Dampier the Buccaneer

> *The creak of the timbers and the lap of the waves; that's music, mates.*

West Country farmer William Dampier became one of the most famous swashbucklers of them all. *Born in West Coker near Yeovil in 1651, William was orphaned at an early age, but finished his education thanks to his father's employer, Sir John Helyar. Sir Helyar then sent the youngster to the family's sugar plantations in Jamaica, but Dampier soon become bored by the life and boarded a schooner bound for North America, eventually becoming a lumber-jack in Canada.*

Tiring of that life too, Dampier returned to England, joined the Royal Navy and was sent to map the northern coastline of Australia in the ship *The Cygnet*. As a result he was the first Englishman to land and trade with local Aboriginal tribes for fresh kangaroo meat and named Dampier Archipelago, Kings Sound and Sharks Bay in 1688. He was amazed by how the Aborigines' boomerangs could bring down birds in flight.

On his return voyage via the Philippines, he stopped for freshwater on an island, and named it *The Duke of Grafton's Isle* after his wife's family.

More than 80 years later Captain Cook was to use Dampier's navigation charts when seeking Van Diemen's Land, which was renamed Tasmania after the island was granted the right to self-government in 1856, having been under Dutch and then British rule up until that point.

Dampier's drawings of foliage and habitat around the world became famous. In order to protect them from harm, such as when he crossed the isthmus at Panama, he kept them rolled up, inside his silver-topped cane.

The remains of a Naval vessel on which Dampier was shipwrecked in 1701, the *H.M.S. Roebuck*, has recently been salvaged at Clarence bay, Ascension Island in the Atlantic Ocean. He and his crew survived only by living off land crabs, boobies and goats. The huge clam shell that he kept as part of his research can be seen today on display at Portsmouth Maritime Museum.

Dampier was rescued from Ascension Island by a pirate ship that had called in to collect fresh water and was bound for Plymouth. After 12 years of freebooting, he eventually returned to England, only to find that his wife had abandoned the family home of Arlington House, which was on the site of the present-day Buckingham Palace.

Having been forced to sell his manservant due to his penniless state, the destitute Dampier made his way back to Bristol to head up an expedition to the South Seas, once again financed by Thomas Goldney. This venture was unsuccessful, and chased by his debtors he joined Rogers in yet another attempt to capture a Spanish treasure ship. That too ended in failure and Dampier died in poverty in the East End of London, and was buried in an unmarked grave in 1715.

Dampier is the only pirate to have his portrait in the National Portrait Gallery. In the parish church of Dampier's birthplace, East Coker, Somerset, you can see a brass plaque recording his remarkable exploits as a buccaneer and explorer.

Dampier's slave, Prince Jeoly, was the eldest son of a tribal leader from the East Indies. Jeoly was heavily tattooed, and immediately created a stir amongst the ladies back at Court in London who covered their lower arms with similar tattoos as a fashion statement. This led to the ladies wearing heavy jewellery to hide the controversial artwork on state occasions.

Prince Jeoly inspired the character Man Friday in Daniel Defoe's book *Robinson Crusoe*.

Dampier awaits the arrival of Selkirk at the Llandoger Trow

Long John Silver the Scoundrel

William Hatley, landlord of the Hole in the Wall tavern in Bristol, kept a sharp eye on his treasure chest. The one-legged scoundrel was keen to see that it was loaded quickly aboard his sloop moored on the quayside at Welsh Back.

His scullery maid and his parrot, Captain Flint, acted as lookouts from the upstairs window. The previous night Hatley had made a great deal of money from organising a press gang for Captain King who lived across the River Avon on Redcliffe Parade and needed a motley crew for his slave ship, *The Benin*.

Hatley knew the customs officers in nearby Queens Square would be after him as soon as they heard the news. He was sending his treasure chest back home to his wife in Africa, with 400 silver coins that he had saved over the years of swashbuckling.

Hatley was a good friend of Robert Louis Stephenson, and inspired the author's most famous character, Long John Silver in the novel Treasure Island. The actor Robert Newton portrayed him in the 1950 film adaptation of the book, right down to his West Country accent. Hatley's notoriety as the inspiration for the character was so strong that the actor's son visited the Hole in the Wall pub in 2008 for a reunion.

The central character in the novel was the young Jim Hawkins, a descendant of the famous Hawkins family of Plymouth. Another was Israel Hands, named after a youth who sailed with Blackbeard after both youths had been press ganged by Silver. On his Captain's death, Hands returned to Bridgewater only to be seized and hung as a pirate at Taunton Assizes.

Press gangs were an awful part of seafaring deemed necessary by the captains who lived in the houses directly opposite the Hole in the Wall tavern. Recruiting experienced seamen was a huge challenge, as the men knew they may not return. In stormy conditions they could be swept overboard, while ruthless captains were known to throw sailors to the waiting sharks below on reaching their destination to avoid having to pay them.

To overcome this labour shortage the Captains could signal to the Hole in the Wall to offer free drinks to the masses. When the word got around, the pub would be packed with potential able seamen.

Hatley, who went by the nickname used by Robert Louis Stephenson's character, would keep watch through a hole in the wall with his spyglass and a shout would go out: *"Press gang!"*

Captain King's men would row across the river armed with hefty sticks and entrap many a drunken individual. By the time the Navy entered the tavern in search of sailors to press into service, the motley crew would already be hidden in the cellars.

The men would wake up the next day with sore heads, aboard slaver ships bound for Bantry Bay,

Press gangs at the Hole in the Wall

"Ruthless captains threw sailors to the waiting sharks below to 'avin' to pay 'em"

Ireland – the first leg of their journey across the Atlantic. On occasion they would mutiny and kill the captain, becoming outlaws and electing their own captain. As pirates they would sometimes head towards the Golden Guinea coast of Africa to attack slavers that were at anchor, occupied with loading slaves. The prizes would be the small bags of gold dust used in trading negotiations with the tribal African Kings.

Bristol men felt safe in Ireland since the invasion led by King Henry II in 1171 ensured no rival Norman dynasty would be established on the offshore island. The king's large fleet had set sail from the Quay of de Clare Street, led by the formidable Richard de Clare, Earl of Pembroke. De Clare was known as Strongbow by his men due to his skill with a long bow.

As a result, pirates returning with bounty would jump ashore at Bantry, the deep water port in Ireland, to avoid the sharp eyes of custom officers waiting for them back in their home port of Bristol.

They often ended up marrying into the impoverished local gentry who were only too glad to welcome a pirate as a new son in law pirate, no doubt rubbing their hands with glee at the thought of all those ill-gotten doubloons.

Sir John Hawkins the Privateer

John Hawkins was the great grandson of Eleanor of Lancaster, a Plantagenent and descendant of Osbert de Hawking 1154.

The family had relocated from Dorchester to Tavistock on the River Tamar, where John was born in 1475. John grew up and married Joan Amadas, the daughter of the Sergeant of Arms to Henry VIII.

The king had been angry and dismayed when he lost his great flagship the *Mary Rose* in Portsmouth harbour, with many of the 400 crewmen drowned below decks. Being top-heavy, it shipped water through the open gun ports on the lower of the three gun decks as it turned to engage the enemy, and had keeled over. You can examine the wreck in Portsmouth museum.

As a result, Henry VIII granted John the lease on the Norman de Valletort shipyard estates in Plymouth on the proviso that he would develop a new type of gunship. This super ship was intended to beat off threats of a Spanish Invasion, and needed to be lower in the waterline, faster and more maneuverable than the large, top-heavy Spanish galleons.

John Hawkins' son William was born in 1495 and grew up to become a successful sea-captain. William became Lord of the manor of Sutton Vale tort and made three voyages to Brazil. He married Joan Trelawney, and their son John was born in 1532. John was destined to become a famous Elizabethan admiral who would do his father proud.

At this time, the French Huguenots were fleeing France's ports and relocating to Plymouth and Bristol as Britain's first registered refugees. They brought with them the expertise of sailing to the Guinea coast of Africa and capturing and enslaving the black people who lived there.

"'e was knighted and made up to Admiral for 'is part in the defeat of the Spanish Armada."

In 1562, backed by a cartel of Bristol merchants, Hawkins sailed on his first slave trading expedition in the *Solomon* and two other ships, with a crew of 100 men. These included his young cousin Francis Drake. They returned after transporting 310 black slaves to the Spanish in the Caribbean and so established the profitable, if heinous, trade triangle.

In 1564 Queen Elizabeth I showed an interest in Hawkins' voyages and supplied him with a huge 700-ton ship, the *Jesus of Lubeck*. On his first expedition aboard the *Jesus*, Hawkins' returned with a 60 per cent profit through transporting 400 slaves taken from Sierra Leon.

John Hawkins was knighted and made up to Admiral in 1588 for his part in the defeat of the Spanish Armada. His coat of arms features a bound black slave, depicting the unsavoury source of his wealth. In 1596 he died of a fever whilst sailing off Porto Bello, Panama.

As his protégée, Drake was to continue the fight against the Spanish and was given permission to use the old fort of Trematon from the deValletort estate on the other side of the Tamar river as a base. This was to mark the beginning of a new chapter in British privateering.

Sir John Hawkins fortified the approaches to Plymouth Sound to ward off the French pirate raids, creating a safe haven where the Pilgrim Fathers sought sanctuary in 1620 when one of their two ships sailing from Southampton down the English channel sprang a leak and became unseaworthy. As a result, all 120 passengers seeking a new life across the Atlantic had to transfer from the *Speedwell* onto one overcrowded ship, the *Mayflower*.

They eventually set sail again on July 22nd with fresh provisions that included barrels of Somerset apples from the cider farms. The *Mayflower* reached the American coast within 66 days, and they established the new colony near Cape Cod, naming it Plymouth.

Their efforts at colonisation and establish the new Puriton religion had been resisted by Catholic Spain on the continent and the English king James I.

Many did not survive the first winter including Francis Eaton of Bristol, and as they reached the point of starvation they were befriended by the local natives who fed them and showed them how crops could be grown. This led to a Thanksgiving Day, which is still commemorated in North America every year.

"His coat of arms features a bound black slave, depicting the unsavoury source of his wealth."

The seas around Cape Cod became infamous for piracy, with the new colonies dependant on friendly pirates bringing in fresh supplies. In return they offered a safe haven to the pirates.

In 1715, Samuel Bellamy of Exeter was financed by a group of local merchants to sail out of Plymouth and capture a Spanish treasure ship off the Massachusetts coastline. He left behind a pregnant girlfriend, Maria Hallet, in Eastham Massachusetts, promising to return with riches.

After successfully taking the *Wydah*, an English three-masted slave ship full of silver bullion and jewels off Cape Cod, Bellamy's ship sank on the reef and almost all hands were lost, including Richard Nolan who had previously sailed with Blackbeard as quartermaster. There were only two survivors, including Welshman Thos Davies, the ship's carpenter, who wrote his memoirs in Boston jail

In 1984 the ship was found in a remarkable state of preservation, buried in the silt. It has given up many of its secrets about living conditions on board a pirate vessel of the period.

The port of Plymouth was also famous as being the embarkation point of one of the UK's most successful pirates, Francis Drake, who sailed out of Plymouth Sound more than a century earlier.

The Hawking Coat of Arms

Sir Francis Drake the Circumnavigator

John Russell, of Kingston Russell Manor, Dorset was the son of Alice Sydenham of Devon and traded with Spain as a wine merchant, sailing out of Weymouth harbour.

In 1506 he rescued a young woman from a shipwreck in Weymouth Bay. The woman turned out to be Princess Juana, the youngest daughter of Isabella, the Spanish queen who had funded the voyage of Columbus to seek the Indies, instead reaching the southern islands of the Americas.

Russell spoke fluent Spanish and having revived the princess, he took her to his cousin's house, Wolfeton Manor, to recuperate. As soon as he discovered her identity and strategic importance to the Crown, Russell escorted the princess straight to London. Russell soon became a favourite at Court, attracting the attention of King Henry VII, whose eldest son, Prince Arthur, aged 15, had married Juana's sister, Catherine of Aragon in 1501. Five months after the wedding, Prince Arthur died, and to maintain the valuable relationship with Spain, Henry VIII then took his brother's place and married Catherine. He enlisted the talented multilingual Russell as a negotiator when he invaded France in 1522.

Russell lost an eye during the ensuing siege of Morlaix and was knighted for his service to the Crown, as well as being granted many estates. These included the seven-acre Covent Garden in London and Woburn Abbey in Bedford, where he resided in 1550 taking the title Duke of Bedford. He was also appointed Marquis of Tavistock, Devon, where he had been given Tavistock Abbey, along with the 30 manors belonging to the abbey.

For three generations the Drake family had leased Crowndale Farm, a small holding of 180 acres, from the Abbey on the banks of the River Tavy. Edmund Drake was a lay preacher, who named his firstborn son Francis after the son of the Marquis. Unfortunately in 1548 Edmund was had up for highway robbery, and he fled to the east coast on the back of a horse and cart. Young Francis joined the household of his uncle Admiral William Hawkins in Plymouth, where he was educated with his cousin John. They sailed together to Tenerife and other Spanish and French ports, and realised that foreign ships and cargoes could soon be separated from their owners, thus learning the art of piracy.

By 1565 Drake was in his early 20s and had saved enough money to buy trade goods and travel on a Hawkins ship to the Guinea coast of West Africa, returning with gold, ivory and spices including pepper. This was the start of a remarkable career that has made him one of the most famous sea captains of British history.

Just across the River Tamar from Plymouth was Saltash Point, where the Normans had built Trematon Castle from which to control the entrance into Plymouth harbour. This did not deter Danish raiders who in 1172 plundered Tavistock Abbey and seized many livestock and women.

For Drake this remote medieval castle with its private slipway was the ideal place to store emeralds, gold and silver treasures stolen from the Spanish bullion ships such as the *Neustra Senora de la Conception*, seized off Ecuador, South America.

By 1580 Drake had unloaded more than 20 tons of silver, 80 lbs of gold doubloons and 13 full cases of jewels into the dungeons of the castle from his ship the *Golden Hind*.

In 1569 Drake married Mary Newman, a Saltash girl. The 14th century cottage where she was born still stands in Culvert Street. Sadly, 12 years after their marriage began, Mary died.

John Wintour was a leading Bristol sea captain and merchant, and a friend of Francis Drake. To continue seafaring, Drake needed to enlist the backing of the West Country's most powerful families, and gain Queen Elizabeth's approval, albeit unofficial, to attack the Spanish flotilla. An opportunity arose in July 1571 when he sailed up the River Severn to visit the Wintour family at their fortified White Cross Manor, Lydney. There the Wintours employed 500 woodcutters to supply timber from the Forest of

> *He enjoyed a fight and this time his foe would be an Englishman*

Dean to the Navy for shipbuilding. John's son William became Treasurer to the Royal Navy. The Wintour family introduced Drake to the Berkeley family, who in turn invited Drake to visit them at their great castle, where the queen would be attending a banquet. So he sailed across the river to Berkeley Creek from his little riverside property at Gatcombe Creek, now the Sloop Inn.

Drake's proposal was to mutual advantage and Elizabeth pledged him 1,000 crowns to bring her the Spanish treasures.

During his grand circumnavigation of the globe, Drake landed in San Francisco Bay for fresh water supplies, trading an English dog, pig and grain seeds with the Indians, and claiming California on behalf of Queen Elizabeth.

Although authorised by the Queen as a privateer to attack and impoverish the Spanish he was always careful to ask when back in his home port if she was still on the throne and to check that England was not yet ruled by the Catholics. If the Queen had lost her place in the monarchy, he could have been imprisoned and executed for his acts against the Spanish Catholics on her behalf. He had already lost two of his crewmen, who happened to be his cousins, to the Spanish. The pair had been taken in the battle off Panama and transported back to the Spanish city of Cádiz to be crucified in the public plaza.

Sir Francis tucks away his treasure from prying eyes

On his arrival back in Greenwich to report to the Queen, Drake was not surprised to find she was under pressure by King Phillip of Spain to have him, *el Drago*, put to death.

The treasure hoard hidden in Trematon Castle was larger than that held in the tower of London and ensured his survival. The queen settled for 10 per cent of his wealth and knighted him instead of executing him, equipping the circumnavigator with her own ship to continue his activities, providing his did so *quietly*. The backers of his voyage got back £47 for every £1 they put in.

Drake died of yellow fever at sea in the Caribbean in 1596.

Sir Walter Raleigh the Treasure Seeker

Walter Raleigh of Sidmouth was a kinsman of the extended Drake family. He was destined to voyage to the new world, sponsored by wealthy the Bristol merchants in return for a share of the spoils. These business men included Robert Aldworth who financed risky voyages and the colonisation of the Boston area of America.

By 1620, the group of merchants had formed the Plymouth & Bristol Company under a charter with King James I. Since their support of Cabot's voyage in 1497 to the simply named Newfoundland, the race against the Spanish to acquire new markets had intensified into open hostilities and piracy.

Walter was a handsome ladies' man and a charmer. Introduced by family members into the court at London, he soon upset the Queen Elizabeth I by dallying with her affections and then marrying her lady-in-waiting in secret. On discovering this, the jealous Queen ensured the couple spent their honeymoon locked up in the Tower of London. Following their release, Raleigh's enemies kept him as far away from the queen as possible by appointing him Minister of Mining for Devon and Cornwall, as well as the vice admiral charged with keeping the Spanish at bay.

In 1584 Raleigh brought back two new world natives named Manteo and Wanchese from Roanoke island off Carolina and paraded them at Court. Manteo soon proved his worth by helping ease the strained relationships between the native Americans and the invading British.

By 1585 Raleigh had made enough money with the backing of the Bristol cartel to embark on a private voyage and established a new colony that he named Virginia after the Virgin Queen.

In 1588 he donated the well-armed *Ark Royal* to lead the English fleet against the Spanish Armada. The ship was used by the Navy for 50 years, and played such an important role that many naval warships have since borne her name.

"...he brought back a root crop that was to become known as the potato..."

Whenever Raleigh found himself in need of a hiding place he would flee to Radford Castle, Plymouth, where he had an understanding with the lady of the manor, Mary Sydenham.

In 1590 Raleigh gave Mary a unique thank-you gift: a set of 22 silver plates taken from a Spanish galleon on its way back home to Cádiz from plundering the silver mines of Potosi, Peru. In 1645 the Sydenham family, who supported the King of England, were concerned that Cromwell would ransack their man-

sion on his way marching south from the siege of Bristol Castle. They sent a cart with their loyal footman and all the family silver up into bleak, remote Dartmoor to bury it.

Their faithful servant was caught on the return journey and tortured by the Roundheads but would not reveal his secret, so the location of the actual burial spot died with him.

During his travels, Raleigh spent much of his time searching for gold, and soon found other, more agricultural treasures. From the Caribbean he brought back a root crop that was to become known as the potato, as named by Columbus who introduced it into Spain in 1492. Raleigh established the very first potato plantation in Ireland on his 49,000-acre estate at Youghal, County Cork.

He also brought back a weed that he had seen the native Americans in Florida set fire to and then inhale. The natives had made him share the pipe of peace and he discovered how relaxing it could be. He demonstrated this new discovery at the home of the Constable of Bristol Castle at Acton Court and then introduced it to the Bristol merchants at the main trading place on the Nails outside the corn market, now known as St Nicks.

Far from being concerned about the health risks, the British public believed the smoke kept the Plague at bay. It soon caught on and was selling well at Malmesbury Market at 1p per pipe. The pipes were designed to be thrown away once used, which is why you can still find the broken pipe bowls and stems in the gardens of the Fishponds area of Bristol, near the former pottery kilns.

Since Roman days, grapes had been grown in the fertile Severn valley, and this was an ideal place to plant this new crop. Several plantations were soon established by the local landowners.

"He was found hiding in his bolt hole, a secret room behind the Tudor panelling in Radford Castle near Plymouth."

Elizabeth I soon realised that she could not keep the profits of these landowners under control and decided to ban it in England, instead growing it in Virginia so she could import it and create a new tax revenue. The landowners were reluctant to cease growing this lucrative crop so she sent her soldiers to burn down the estates, much to the dismay of her subjects.

The Wills brothers from Salisbury travelled to Bristol to seek their fortune and, with help from their sister who was already established on Bristol

Bridge, set up their first retail outlet on Redcliffe hill. This was to become the Imperial Tobacco Company, which made its fortune from the Virginia pipe tobacco label.

Raleigh did not prosper so well; he lost his eldest son, also named Walter, in 1616 in a fight with the Spanish. In 1618 he rashly promised King James I great riches in an attempt to keep out of prison, but returned from his voyage empty handed.

He was found hiding in his bolt hole, a secret room behind the Tudor panelling in Radford Castle near Plymouth.

As centuries passed, many impoverished generations searched the large mansion and its secret passages for the original treasure map, but to no avail.

In 1823 a farm labourer high up on the hills put his pitchfork through one of the large silver plates, and they have now been recovered to rest easy in the British Museum, valued at £1 million.

After being dragged unceremoniously from his hiding place, Raleigh was executed in public. His severed head was embalmed and given to his wife, who carried it around with her in a red leather bag until she died many years later. It is now buried with the body of their son Carew.

Sir Walter introduces the weed at the Nails

Lord Stuckley the Lion-tamer

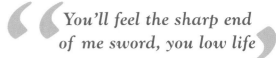

When the rampant King Henry VIII visited Lord Maurice at Thornbury Castle near Bristol, he turned his attention to the Lord's daughter, Lady Mary Berkeley. Though his advances were entirely unwelcome, they were difficult to refuse, as any such liaison would ensure titles and lands for any resulting offspring, legitimate or not.

Mary gave birth to two of the King's sons, John Parrot in 1526 and Thomas Stuckley in 1527. Both were sent to live in remote parts of the West Country to be brought up and tutored by the local impoverished squires, who were granted a title and estates as payment for their efforts.

Sir John Parrot went to live in South Wales, while his brother, Sir Thomas Stuckley was brought up in North Devon, separated by the Bristol Channel. They were banned from affairs of state by their half-sister Queen Elizabeth, which proved a problem as the two boys inherited their father's stature and rebellious attitude, and soon turned to piracy in the Bristol Channel.

At Hartland Priory, Stuckley soon sided with the French as a soldier of fortune against Spain and then plotted to invade England to claim the throne with the French army landing at Falmouth to march to London. The plans came to nothing and he returned home to marry the heiress Anne Curtis to pay off his debts.

In 1558, he was accused of piracy but was saved from imprisonment by his half-sister. She decided to get rid of this threat to her Reign by appointing him Governor of Florida far, far away. Armed with the Royal Warrant he set sail from Greenwich with 300 men in five ships, but was distracted when he came across a fleet of Flemish ships in the English Channel and decided to attack. The ships were returning from an expedition to Africa with a collection of wild animals for the French king's new zoo in Paris.

Finding no gold on board, Stuckley let the ships go after seizing a lion and two leopards as mementos. He kept the animals chained up on the deck.

Stuckley soon realised his error in judgement as the beasts became terribly seasick and the crew were too frightened of them to perform their tasks. Stuckley sailed into the nearest port, Plymouth harbour, where he tied the lion and leopards up the Hoe and abandoned them. The local population flocked down to the quayside to see the spectacle.

This type of activity was more to Stuckley's liking than going off to colonise new lands, so he dropped anchor in Dartford before moving on down the coast. Eventually he settled in Falmouth, which was a wonderful base from which to sail to the Azores and capture Spanish treasure ships.

Highly embarrassed by his roguish behaviour, the Queen outlawed her half-brother in 1565 so he couldn't endanger delicate negotiations between the English Crown and King Philip of Spain.

"Finding no gold on board, Stuckley let the ships go after seizing a lion and two leopards as mementos."

In 1571, Stuckley sailed to Rome and had an audience with Pope Pious V, with whom he plotted a Roman Catholic invasion of Ireland. The Pope was keen to expel all the Protestants, and Stuckley wanted to seize back his former estates that had been taken due to his unlawful activities.

Unfortunately the venture was unsuccessful, so in 1578 he collaborated with the 22-year-old King Sebastian of Portugal whose great Armada of 500 ships were on their way to invade Morocco. They were overwhelmed by Sultan Abul el Malek's superior forces. A cannonball blew off Stuckley's legs and he and the king were dragged ashore and killed.

Stuckley's only son William survived and the family still run the estate at Hartland Abbey with cream teas a speciality, and no mention of their earlier dastardly deeds.

Lady Killigrew the Temptress

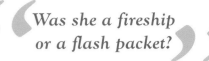
When Mary de Wolverston met John Killigrew, they knew they were destined to be together. Mary was the daughter of Suffolk pirate Philip de Wolverston and John was the son of a privateer — his family had made a lot of money through the deeds of pirates, building a big mansion named Arwenack Houses with the ill-gotten proceeds.

The couple met at Court when Mary was a lady-in-waiting to Queen Elizabeth I. After marrying and moving to Cornwall, the pair had their own lighthouse built at Lands End to monitor the shipping activity around the Cornish peninsular, levying a fee on passing vessels. Ironically John then became a vice-admiral, responsible for removing French and Dutch pirates from British waters by whatever means necessary, however brutal.

Mary, now Lady K, was far from your average, well-behaved Elizabethan wife and in 1583, whilst the Admiral was at sea chasing French pirates, she decided to engage in a little piracy herself.

From the top floor of Arwenack House, Lady K's mother-in-law Lady Elizabeth spied a potential target, the Spanish ship *Marie of San Sebastion* that was sheltering from a storm in Falmouth harbour below.

With her mother-in-law's guidance, Lady K press-ganged her household staff into becoming sailors and ordered them to capture the ship and its valuable cargo of bullion bound for Germany.

One advantage Lady K had over most pirates was her feminine wiles and she enticed the captain of *Marie of San Sebastion*, Philip de Orozo to accompany her ashore. She took de Orozo to the Penryn tavern, got him drunk, provided him with a couple of loose women to keep him amused, and then went back and ransacked his ship. She and her household staff cum sailors killed the crew and dumped them overboard. Her servants John Hawkins and Henry Kendall sailed the ship to Ireland where it fetched a good price with no questions asked.

Several large sea chests of silver were taken ashore and buried in the grounds of Arwenack Manor. They have never been publicly recovered and may lie there still.

Despite her husband's best endeavours, Lady K and her servants were brought to trial at Launceston Assizes and sentenced to death. Hawkins and Kendall were hung on the gallows.

At the eleventh hour Lady K was reprieved by the queen, who probably realised she might need the future support and ships of West Country pirates to fight off a threatened Spanish invasion.

Lady K's embarrassed husband was allowed to take her back to Falmouth after his dominating mother paid the large court fine, counting it out in the stolen Spanish silver.

Sir Walter Raleigh once stayed overnight at the manor homeward bound from the Guinea coast, but he moved on quickly, complaining that he found the accommodation too basic.

Lady Killigrew was pleased with the arrangements she had made for the Captain

Bonny Anne Bonney & Barefoot Mary

When she was still a young woman, Anne Bonney met a larger-than-life character by the name of Captain Jack Rackham and took to a new and exciting life. Though married, bonny Anne was soon seduced by Rackham's wild ways, and left behind her husband who promptly took to drink.

Rackham had been one of the pirates pardoned by Woodes Rogers in the Bahamas, and the pair of lovers fled the island one night by stealing a ship in the harbour. Anne flaunted her naked body to lure the guards away from the ship while Rackham ran onboard and made preparations to sail. Then they disappeared into the night together, leaving the guards baffled and, no doubt, sorely disappointed.

In 1718 they took an English ship sailing out of Brixham, Devon to the West Indies and took captive another extraordinary character, Mary Read, who dressed as a man. The two women became attracted to each other but Jack did not complain as they all shared the same small bunk.

In 1720, after acquiring a lot of booty, their ship was cornered by a British frigate off Jamaica. Mary, who had seen service as a British soldier on the Continent whilst disguised as a man, fought like a devil with her cutlass, whilst Anne used her pair of pistols, but to no avail.

Rackham and some of the drunken crew were found skulking below in the hold, and they were all caught, taken ashore, brought to trial and sentenced to death at Port Royal Assizes. Rackham was hung from the scaffold at execution point. The women escaped execution because they were pregnant, probably both by Rackham.

Maria Lyndsey of Plympton became another famous female pirate in the 16th century after meeting and marrying the dashing Captain Eric Cobham, a member of a famous Poole family who still trade in Dorset. For some years she accompanied her husband as he engaged in piracy around the south west coast of England. They made a frightful, formidable pair.

Maria was known for walking around the deck barefoot, dressed in buckskin breeches and with a pair of pistols tucked into a broad leather belt around her plentiful waist. She was skilful with a dagger and delighted in tying her captives up in sacks and tossing them overboard. She sometimes poisoned them when they were being held captive in the hold of her ship. On one occasion she stabbed to death the captain of a Liverpool brig they had captured on the high seas.

The two horrors seized a ship in Bridport, armed it with fourteen guns and then took a French ship full of brandy off Portland Bill. Soon after that they took over another ship that yielded £40,000 in merchandise. One by one, Mary forced the men off the end of a plank with her cutlass and then drove the ship onto the rocks at Pennsylvania Cove where their bodies were washed ashore. You can see their graves in Ope churchyard above the beach, their tombstones carved with the skull and crossbones.

Having amassed a fortune, Maria and Cobham considered buying an estate near Lytchett Matravers, Poole, but because they had upset Poole's parliament member by preying on the towns' profitable fishing trade, they decided instead to leave England and live in style in a French chateau in Le Havre, which they bought from the Duc de Chartres. The place had its own harbour, in which they moored their ship.

Following a series of small raids along the French coastline, the Cobhams retired in France. Eric became a respectable magistrate but, filled with remorse for having lived such a sinful life, Maria committed suicide by taking arsenic. She died barefoot but dressed up in the clothes of a Royal Navy officer that she had forced to walk the plank, a fitting apology for her many evil deeds.

She enjoyed the spectacle of forcing men to walk the plank

Admiral de Pellow the Avenger

Thomas Pellow was only 11 years old when his uncle John, a gruff sea-dog suggested that he joined the crew of the *Francis* to sail to Genoa, Italy, with a hold filled with salted pilchards that had been caught off Falmouth that night.

Leaving Penryn in 1715, they set sail for the Scilly Isles, but became trapped by Moroccan pirates, taken prisoner and shackled together. The seven members of the crew ended up in the Moroccan city of Salé at a North African slave auction.

Young Pellow was separated from his shipmates and sent to the dungeons of the Meknes, the great Sultan Ismail's fort in Algiers, where he was to polish armour and sharpen swords.

Regularly, he was taken outside into the courtyard and strapped upside down to a pole, and then his bare feet were beaten until raw. This punishment is called bastinado, and after several months of this torture the young man resorted to taking the Islamic faith to prevent it happening again. He renounced the Christian faith and became fluent in Arabic. He was then sent to work in stables that housed 12,000 horses.

Pellow came to the notice of Sultan Moulay Ismail. Aged 70, the sultan had an anger management prob-

lem. When he donned his yellow robes in the morning, the people around him knew they risked death at his hand – often he would lash out at the grooms with his scimitar and cut off their arms. On one occasion Pellow witnessed him sawing in two brothers in half.

The tyrannical sultan flogged Pellow often but kept him from death as he spoke English and could be useful. Soon he was to interrogate the white-skinned girls that had been kidnapped from Irish and West Country coastal villages. His duties included inspecting their teeth and body before declaring whether they were suitable for training to join the harem of 500 maidens. They could only survive if they caught the eye of the Sultan and gave him pleasure. Only 500 girls were allowed to remain in the harem at any time, so when a new girl joined another was usually put to death. Their Nubian guards had their testicles removed at an early age, so posed no threat.

After marrying one of the girls that the Sultan had rejected, thus saving her life, Pellow had a daughter. However, he was still desperate to escape and, disguised as travelling healer, he trekked through the mountains, from one isolated village to another. He noticed many blue eyed children, resulting from forced liaisons with European sailors. When he eventually reached the Atlantic coast, Pellow bribed an

Irish captain with a handful of gold and persuaded the man to drop him off at Gibraltar. From here he managed to return to Penryn on October 15th 1738, some 21 years after he was captured aged 11.

At first his elderly parents did not recognise the grown man as their son, but once he had convinced them of who he was, they welcomed him in. He returned to the Christian faith and took a local woman as his wife, starting a new family.

> *"He was still desperate to escape and, disguised as travelling healer, he trekked through the mountains, from one isolated village to another."*

The Pellow family would not forget the injustices that had been done to Thomas. He wrote a book on his escapades, in which he detailed the fortifications of the fort at Algiers, showing the defensive gun battery cross fire positions with a blind spot. This was to become a key part of his descendants' revenge.

More than 80 years later, one of Pellow's great grandson's, Edward, joined the Royal Navy. He rose through the ranks and became the officer responsible for controlling the Mediterranean with Horatio Hornblower as his flag officer. They were despatched

> *I wouldn't touch her with a barge pole, shipmates*

by the Admiralty in 1816 to the Barbary coast in *HMS Queen Charlotte*, armed with 100 guns to bombard the fort of Algiers and release 1,642 European slaves, including some Americans.

Edward's squadron was joined by Dutch and French warships for this retaliatory raid, using the information Thomas Pellow had provided decades before of the blind spot in defence of the fortifications. Bringing their ships to anchor only 80 yards offshore they besieged the town.

The Dey of Algiers was facing defeat and angry that the French had joined forces with the English. They sent men into town to bring up the French Consul General to the ramparts, where they removed his boots, bound his feet and wrists and, with his cocked hat, loaded him into a large cannon. Still protesting he was fired onto the deck of the French flagship below in the harbour.

His body parts were splattered across the sails, but his head remained intact and was preserved in a barrel of brandy to be shown to the French Emperor on their return to Paris.

In 1830, the newly elected French King Louis XVIII decided to seek revenge on these troublesome Moors that had been expelled from Spain to the Barbary Coast almost four centuries earlier.

The French Official fired out of the cannon

He sent a huge invading army of 35,000 troops, and Algeria became a French colony for 132 years until General Charles de Gaulle granted them independence in 1958.

Sir Edward was ennobled with the title of Viscount Exmouth and awarded a large family estate in the Teign Valley, Devon. The attractive manor house overlooks the entrance to the harbour and is now council offices. Missing his days as an admiral, he placed a matching pair of ornate cannon taken from Algiers on his front lawn, so that he could sit between them and have the sense of controlling the narrow harbour entrance. Until the day he died, he demanded that sea craft had to salute him before attempting to sail through the run.

Admiral Murat Rais the hostage-taker

In 1580 Jans Jansson of Haarlem, Holland, sailed as a privateer to attack Spanish ships which were supporting the army of the Spanish King Philip II. At that time Holland, along with much of mainland Europe, was owned by the Spanish, and it took the Eighty Year War to restore even part of the land to the control of the Dutch.

In 1618, Jansson was captured by Algerian pirates whilst ashore in Lanzarote in the Canary Islands, and was taken to Morocco. To escape a life of drudgery as a slave, Jansson took up the Islamic faith and became known as Murat Rais, sailing at the head of a large fleet under the crescent flag. He took many hostages back to the port Salé on the North African coast, as Algeria was under siege by the English Navy.

In 1627 he organised a daring raid on the Icelandic capital Rejavik and took 400 hostages.

In 1631, using Lundy Island in the Bristol channel as his base, Rais raided Baltimore coastal village, Ireland with Ottoman troops and took 200 young hostages, locking the older people in the local church and setting it on fire.

Sailing with his eldest son Anthony, Rais met his match in Cornwall. After raiding Poole harbour and setting the town on fire, they sailed down the Devon coastline, raiding Cockington village in Torbay, Brixham and Fowey Harbours, and taking silver from the local churches. The lookouts high up in the church towers rang the warning bells in good time, giving the villagers an opportunity to flee to the fields, a survival tactic they had been using in times of trouble since the Viking raids of the 10th and 11th centuries.

The father and son's troubles had started earlier when they lost one of their fleet of 30 ships on the reef outside Salcombe Harbour and watched helplessly as their shipwrecked sailors struggled through a large swell only to be killed on the shore and buried upright in the sand by local Christians. This beach has since been known as Moorsands.

The wreck, a slave ship with oars, has now been recovered and its treasure, the largest haul of Moorish silver and jewels ever found in England, now lies in the safety of the British Museum.

Sailing home down the coastline the father and son team decided to make one last raid after rounding Lands End. They came ashore at Marazion, Mounts Bay, Penzance, in the falling light. Around 60 local people immediately hid in the church, but were soon discovered by the pirates. As Rais and Anthony loaded their captives onto the ships, the tide turned and they were trapped on the beach. Hearing the warning of the church bell, a crew of angry, drunken local pirates poured out of the taverns of Penryn, well up for some action.

Rais lost his sword in the hand to hand fighting in the surf, and it can now be seen lodged in the framework of the Admiral Benbow Inn, Penzance.

Having barely survived the fray, Anthony decided that his father's risky life was not for him, so in 1629 he married Grietze Reyniers from the town of Wesel on the Rhine and together they sailed from Amsterdam to start a new life in America, joining the other land-owning Dutch settlers at the new Fort of Amsterdam. The large flat island overlooked a deep water port that had been discovered by Hendrick Hudson on behalf of the Dutch in 1625. John Cabot sailing out of Bristol had sheltered there 122 years earlier.

Using some of his father's fortune, Anthony purchased a 200-acre estate at Coney island, Manhattan. He chose that location as it came complete with a private harbour, and the life of piracy proved impossible

> **''e locked the older people in the church an' set fire to it!!''**

to resist as he smuggled goods in right under the noses of the English Navy. The estate was named Turks Island by the locals and a beautifully bound Koran bible from this time is still in the family possession.

The family line continued through the centuries with both Humphrey Bogart and Jackie Kennedy being descendants of Murat Rais the pirate.

Anthony's wife Grietze was following other pioneering members of her family from Wesel, the Ten Broekes. They had been granted an area on the River Hudson known as Beverwyck. It was used for trading with the Mohawk fur trappers, particularly for beaver pelts, and was later renamed Albany after the British seized the land from the Dutch in 1664.

The Duke of York and Albany stayed as a guest of the Ten Broeke family. The result was the establishment of the beaver fur trade in England. On the profits of this venture, the Royal Masonic school was established at Euston, London, in 1788. The large portrait in the school's main hall shows a Mohawkan chief with Anthony Ten Broeke in attendance.

Over 200 years later, the present elder of the family in England is the author of this book, still displaying a few inherited piratical tendencies.

Admiral Murat Rais raids Mounts Bak, Cornwall to capture slaves

Sir Hugh de Marisco the Assassin

"Pirate Island, such a place the like which I never saw"

Lundy Island is named after the Norwegian word for puffin, but it was once just as popular with pirates. The great isolated rock sits in the middle of the Bristol Channel, an ideal base for piracy. It had been a pirate stronghold since 1234, when Sir Hugh de Marisco, formerly a Norman knight, fell out with King Henry III over disputes about his Irish estates and fled from his Gordano valley home.

He took refuge on this remote island, building an almost inaccessible castle on top of the high cliffs. From there the rogue sallied out to intercept passing ships; not only to plunder them of gold and silver but to take victuals, since the island was barren and could not sustain life.

To get revenge for his reduced way of life, de Marisco paid an assassin to murder the king, a fellow Plantagenet. The hooded man got as far as the King's bed-chamber in Oxford, raised his dagger but failed in his act of Regicide – perhaps he had a fit of conscience at just the wrong moment.

Alarmed, the king dispatched a platoon of well-armed soldiers to the port of Clovelly to capture de Marisco. They had paid local seamen to show them the way up the steep cliffs and captured the garrison, which they then put all to death. The Norman knight was strapped by his ankles behind his own horse and taken to the mainland, where he was dragged through the Somerset levels to the high cross at Bristol where the aristocracy was hung as a reminder to the citizens not to go against the king. By then barely alive, de Martisco was taken to the Tower of London and later hung, drawn and quartered.

Lundy was the haunt of pirates other than Marisco, however. Many skeletons have been dug up on the island, including one measuring eight feet two inches in length, which is rumoured to have belonged to Long John Silver, suggesting this may have been the pub landlord turned pirate's final resting place.

The island abounds with strange nicknames such as Puffin Gully, Rat Island, Hell's Gate, Devil's Slide and Mouse Island, but to most it will always be known as Pirate Island.

The Lord of the Manor is dragged back to the King in Oxford from his castle on Lundy Island

Swashbuckling Tales of West Country Pirates | Peter Martin

This act of attempted Regicide had consequences on the West Country

Captain John Cabot the Adventurer

Sir, to be frank with you, I am of those who fly any flag that the occasion may demand

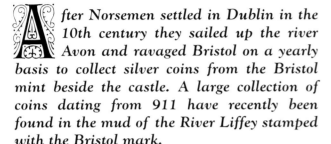

After Norsemen settled in Dublin in the 10th century they sailed up the river Avon and ravaged Bristol on a yearly basis to collect silver coins from the Bristol mint beside the castle. A large collection of coins dating from 911 have recently been found in the mud of the River Liffey stamped with the Bristol mark.

Led by Eric the Red who was fleeing from a charge of manslaughter, the Norse tribes also sailed across to the North American coast in 985 and settled at L'ainse aux Meadows. Here they settled in a pleasant land of meadows and made wine from cranberries, so naming it Vineland.

The valuable Viking sea charts that recorded the dangerous passages were passed down father to son to their descendants in Bristol. As a result sailors from Bristol and Poole crossed the Atlantic from 1320 using this northerly route to prepare and salt fish on the mainland. These hardened men were a valuable source of labour as future pirates.

In 1486 everything changed with the arrival in Bristol of an explorer with the reputation of a pirate. His name was Christopher Columbus and he was known to have taken three Breton vessels off Bordeaux. He stayed as a guest of the powerful shipbuilding family of William Canynges at the mansion on Redcliffe Backs.

Sailing with Bristol seaman to Iceland, Columbus learned their secrets. He approached the Portuguese royals for the funding for a new adventure, and when they refused he returned to Spain where he was financed by Queen Isabella, who pawned her jewels to raise the money for an expedition.

Richard Americke, tax and customs collector for Bristol and a close friend of the King, had built a 50-ton square rigged carvel to sail the Atlantic. The ship was made from sturdy oak cut down from his estate at Weston under Penyard in the Forest of Dean. As the tax collector he named the new ship *Matthew*, the tax collector in the Bible

Americke knew the route well; all he needed was an experienced navigator. Giovanni Cabotto of Geneo, who was bored working in Venice on the sea defences, was the ideal candidate. Known in England as John Cabot, the Italian had learned his seamanship alongside Columbus at the school of navigation in Sitges, Portugal. They'd even shared the tutelage of Prince Henry the navigator, grandson of John of Gaunt. There was a natural rivalry between the two men and they were each eager to prove themselves and be the first to discover new sea routes to China and Japan.

Cabot managed to persuade Henry VII that he could find the westward sea route to China and Japan where the spice routes started before the long and treacherous route overland to Europe. King Henry VII granted Cabot Letters Patent that gave him permission to and find new lands and take them in the king's name.

Cabot was instructed to use Bristol as his home port and bring all goods and profits back to England through the Port of Bristol. He arrived in Bristol in 1494 with his wife and three sons and were housed in St Nicholas Street, in a home belonging to Americke's assistant Arthur Kemeys. In 1495 he made his first attempt to find the sea route to China but was beaten back to Bristol by the weather.

His second and most successful voyage was made in 1497, when he set sail with a crew of 18 men, including his eldest son. In 54 days they arrived at what is now called Newfoundland, having taken the northern route to avoid meeting any Spanish ships as Britain and Spain were not on good terms. The ship then followed the coast of North America, getting as far as Boston before setting off for the return voyage to Bristol. In all they were away for only 70 days

Within two days of landing at Pill on the River Avon, Cabot was celebrated in Court by the King. The naming of the continent America comes from the name of Richard Americke, the major sponsor of the legendary voyage.

The Eve of Departure, May 1497. Cabot and his son watch the preparation of the Matthew at Redcliffe Quay, Bristol

The following year, Cabot set sail with three ships and 500 sailors, many at arms, charged with exploring the coast further south and claiming more lands in the Kings name.

Unfortunately Spanish spy Johannes Day witnessed the meeting and sent information of the impending voyage to Queen Isabella. The parchment was recently found hidden in the back of a drawer in the Spanish archives. Day's messages tally with evidence recovered last century in the secret Vatican archives, revealing details of an expedition led by the cruel and ruthless pirate Alonzo de Hojeda, with instructions to intercept and kill any Englishmen that he found.

In 1486 everything changed with the arrival in Bristol of an explorer with the reputation of a pirate.

Sailing south from Cádiz to a point off the African coast to satisfy the Papal decree of 1493, de Hojeda crossed the Atlantic to the Canary islands. From there he went further eastwards to the Azores to finally reach the South America coast. His vessel reached the island of Margarita in 1499 and immediately started to slaughter the native Indians who lived on houses on stilts in the lagoons.

Americas Vespucci, an Italian noble who was sailing with the expedition, named the place Little Venice after the waterborne city of his native land. The area is now known as Venezuela. At Caracas they intercepted Cabot's depleted fleet of only three ships and 200 men and following his instructions Hojeda butchered all, leaving no survivors.

Dead men tell no tales, but the Spanish Cartographer on the voyage made the mistake of later publishing Cabot's sea charts that they had seized. The charts were complete with several English flags that illustrated Cabot's progress down the eastern seaboard from New York to Florida. Cabot's memorial can now be seen in St Mary's Church, Bristol.

For his decisive if brutal actions, Hojeda was granted six leagues of land in Hispaniola and for the past 500 years the naming of America in the world has been accredited to the Italian Americas Vespucci, when in fact it was named after Americke of Bristol.

It seems that when it comes to pirates, nothing is ever quite as it appears – which isn't really surprising when you consider that every last one of them is a seadog, a rogue and a bloodthirsty varmint with nary an honourable bone in their bodies!

Today in Bristol the replica of the *Matthew* attracts tourists to the harbour in conjunction with the famous *Pirate Walks*. See **www.piratewalks.co.uk**

AMERYKE

As the King's Customs Officer for the Port of Bristol in 1497 and paid Cabot's pension on his return on behalf of the Crown, he would have used the seal below as sheriff of Bristol in 1500. A wealthy merchant financing ventures since 1480 and from his extensive estates including owning 1/3rd of the Manor of Clifton from this estate he would have provided oaks to build the Matthew. As Cabot's main sponsor his escutcheon, above would have been one of the flags John Cabot planted on the "New Found Land" and named "Ameryka" after him. You can still vist the medieval chapel, were both of them prayed, by invitation only on the "Cabot's Heritage Trail". His family originated from the Kings of Gwent.

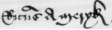

The dawn arrival of Cabot on the New Found Lands where he plants the flags of Venice and Wales (after his sponsor)

West Country Slavers

dd to your library of *Swashbuckling Tales* with **West Country Slavers.**

Lifting the lid on a trade that continues in the footsteps of the Romans, Vikings and every other culture that invaded our small vulnerable island, this remarkable collection examines some of humanity's darkest deeds and brings to light the involvement of prominent West Country families, from the Morgans of Captain Morgan's Rum to the Frys of Fry's Chocolate.

Today, household names such as Cadbury's chocolate and Golden Virginia tobacco continue to remind us of this shady past. The unsavoury details of Bristol's most profitable trade have been covered up for centuries, until now.

Whether you're intrigued by genealogy, human rights or the history of the West Country, this book will make fascinating reading.

Go to **www.swashbucklingtales.info** to order your copy now.

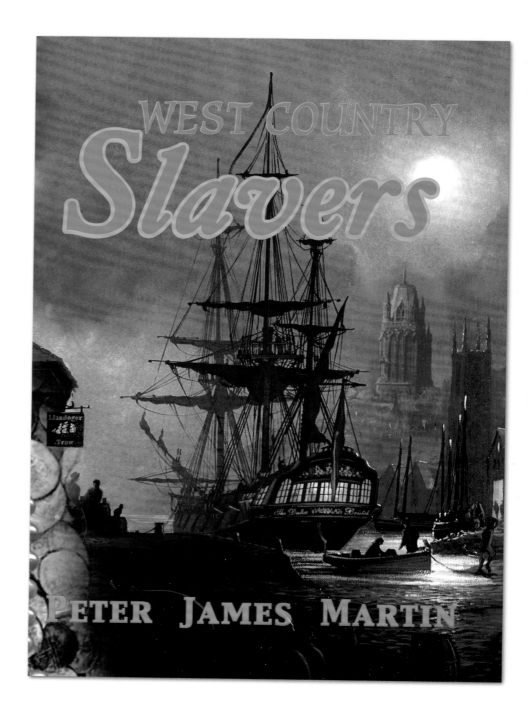